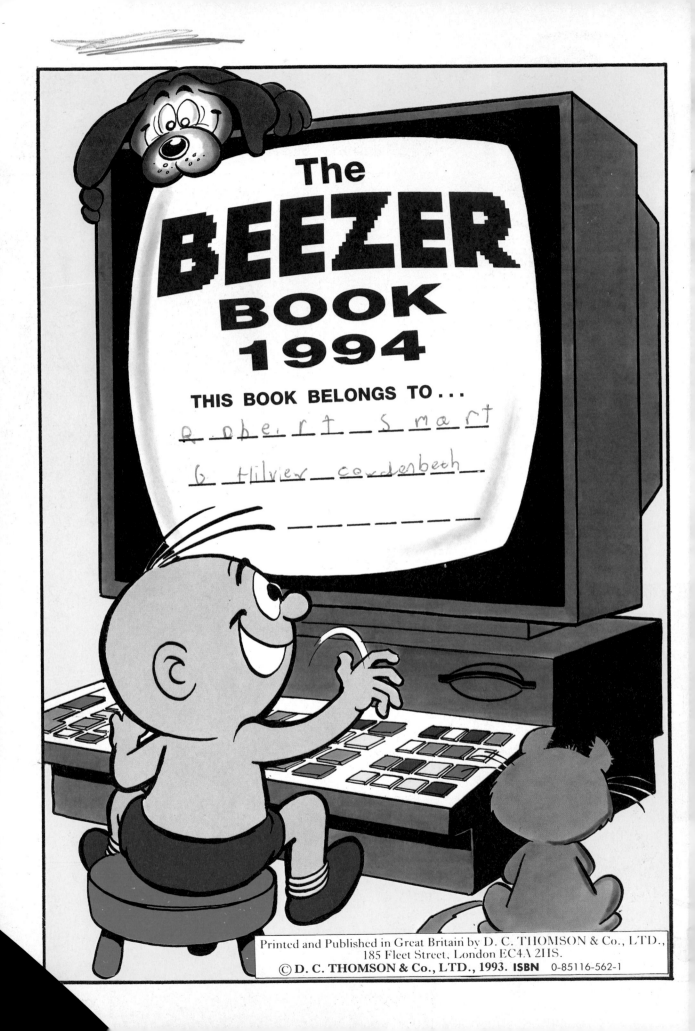

The
BEEZER
BOOK
1994

THIS BOOK BELONGS TO . . .

Robert Smart

G. Hilvier cordenbeth

Printed and Published in Great Britain by D. C. THOMSON & Co., LTD.,
185 Fleet Street, London EC4A 2HS.
© D. C. THOMSON & Co., LTD., 1993. ISBN 0-85116-562-1

GEEZER

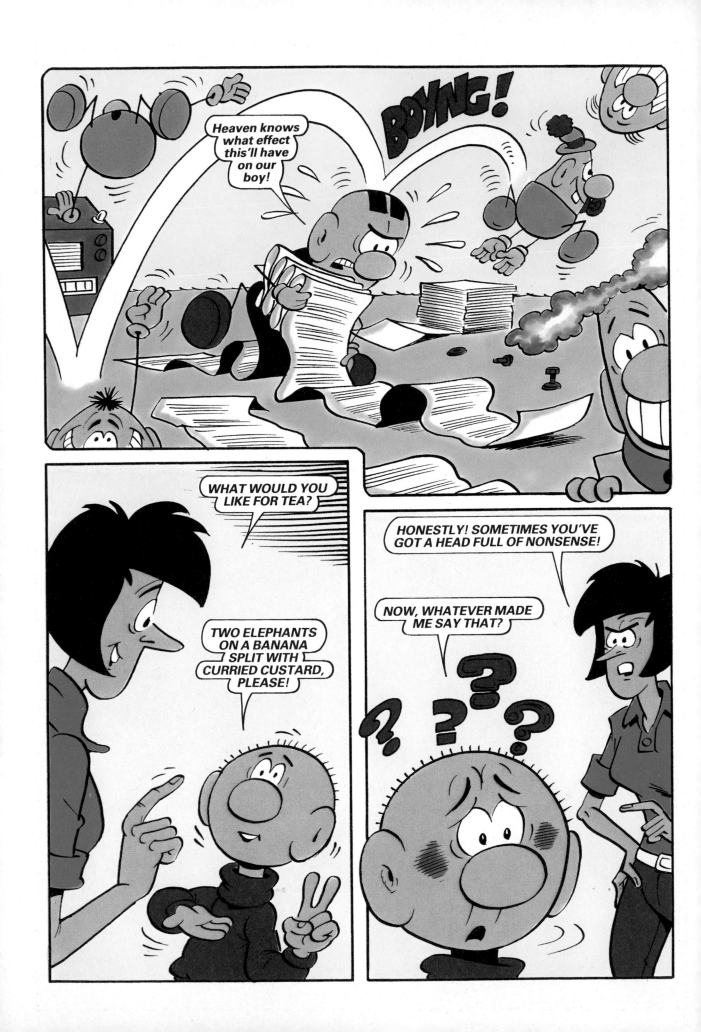

IN THE NEWS

A Scotsman once cycled right round the world — from Ayr, to Ayres rock, in Australia — all for charity.
It must have been an interesting journey. But this interesting . . ? Maybe!

BLINKY in "SANTA'S LITTLE HELPER"

Are we all nice and comfy? Then I'll begin my story. It's called "Santa's Little Helper".

Goody gumdrops.

BLINKY'S DAD

Once upon a time, well, this morning actually, an elf was out collecting a Christmas tree for Santa Claus. It would have been an easy job for him . . .

XMAS TREES FOR SALE

. . . except that young Colin Blinky was getting a tree too.

Ugh!

This'll do me.

Santa was in such a hurry . . .

Hurry up, elf! Mrs Claus will have tea ready.

Taxi drivers are getting ruder all the time.

Baby Crockett

Smashin'!

ALIENS FROM SPACE

Later—

Did you see "The Aliens from Space" on television, Tony?

Yes, it was great.

What would you do if you met an alien?

I'd invite it home for tea.

. . . an' play games.

Would you be scared, Baby?

Me? No way . . .

... I'd make pals with it ...

... an' take it for a nice run in my car ...

... maybe even a game of football.

Mind you, SOME aliens could be scarey, Tony.

You will come with me, Earthlings!

Ulp!

STORMIN' NORMA

Dad's goin' cycling with me.

Well, I'm ready to go!

I'll just die of embarrassment.

Not too tiring, is it?

Nah, it's easy with two cycling.

Yup, sure is.

Aha! I see a way across — we'll do a ramp jump.

ROAD CLOSED!

Up, up and —

—AWAY!

ZOOM!

SMACK!

CLUNK!

I love being out in the fresh air. It's so healthy, isn't it?

She just has to be joking!

The BANANA BUNCH

Gone . . .

. . . but I'll soon find them with my superior brain.

Fatty never drops any food, but he's still easy to track down . . .

. . . he's so heavy.

And he's too fat to get in his hiding place.

Found!

Gottim! Now for the others!

PLOP!

C

HUNT THE BUNCH

Now's your chance to play Hide and Seek. The Bunch are hidden somewhere in this town. Go an' seek 'em, readers.

IN THE NEWS

A survey of our bathtime habits was conducted by a firm of kitchen and bathroom specialists. It made interesting reading. Here are some of the things people do in the soapy suds . . .

Some daydream.

Others eat!

Then there are those who sing!

And the ones who read.

Do you mind?

D-Down, Rover!

Some people keep pets in their baths!

The East Midlands has the largest proportion of whirlpool baths.

Bathtime, Tony!

Of course, there are some who will do all they can to avoid going near a bath!

POTSWORTH & CO.

in "WE AND OUR SHADOWS".

NOW AT THE CARNIVAL—

BLINKY!

your eyes

C'mon, Dad. The carnival's great fun.

Well, okay.

Soon —

Aw, boo! I missed!

POP!

Let me have a go, Dad.

Bad luck, son. You missed, too.

Missed the entire stall!

POP!

No, he didn't. He won a teddy on my stall.

Good old Colin.

Ooo! Ta!

Go and get us some candy floss to celebrate.

Good-oh!

Ben and Nicola's quest finishes later in the Beezer Book.

E

THE

Numskulls

Now let's mess with our boy's sense of TOUCH!

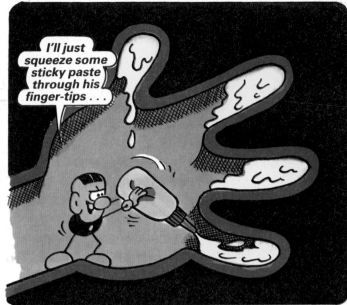

I'll just squeeze some sticky paste through his finger-tips...

...an' let's see what happens!

NICE DOG, MISSUS!

ER... HE SEEMS TO BE A BIT STUCK ON ME!

SHAKE!

EEK! MY TIDDLES!

I SHALL BE SENDING THE DOG PARLOUR'S BILL DIRECT TO YOU!

HOW DID THAT HAPPEN?

Later —

YOU LOOK LIKE YOU'RE IN A TERRIBLE MOOD!

NO WONDER! IT'S BEEN A TERRIBLE DAY!

Who played Arnold Schwarzenegger's brother in "Twins"?

Cheese, butter and milk are all hidden in the grid. All you have to do is find them.

```
C H E E S E
C M U L K O D
R R E L T U B
M M I K L R N
M E Z E H H C
R E T T U B
```

Unscramble these letters to find this European city.

CENVIE

Match these sports stars to the sport in which they compete.
Football, Boxing, Tennis, Cricket.

FRANK BRUNO.

ANDRE AGASSI.

IAN BOTHAM.

JOHN BARNES.

ANSWERS

HOW DID YOU RATE?

0-15 seconds:	Try peeking at the answers next time.
16-30 seconds:	Must try harder.
31-45 seconds:	Not bad.
46-60 seconds:	Good effort.
over 60 seconds:	Congratulations! You're a Master Puzzler!

They've sent two of the crystal splinters back, but they're running out of time.

When a time experiment being carried out by Professor Grant goes terribly wrong, his children Ben and Nicola, have to travel back through time to find all four pieces of the Time Crystal — before space and time disintegrate.

So, you be stowaways. Well, I hates stowaways, but if you work on my ship . . .

. . . you'll be well rewarded.

The crystal!

Later, lad. You has to work afore you gets booty on this pirate's ship.

Ugh. Work!

You set to scrubbing the deck.

Where's my brush?

Oh, not you, lad. I has another job in mind for you — in the crow's nest watching for ships.

Soon—

There's a ship coming, but if I tell the captain he'll attack it.

Then—

We're under attack. Why didn't you give the warning?

Drop dead!

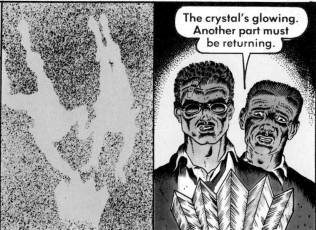

They keep their valuables in here. I bet the crystal is here, too.

The crystal is there.

And HE's in the way.

TIMEQUAKE!

TZANG!

Villain! You shall not point your sword at children while a King's Musketeer lives.

3 . . . 2 . . . 1 . . . now!

They've done it — now you must go back to your own time.

ZZZZAK!

With the crystal back in one piece, time is safe — and you're both home in one piece. It must have been amazing.

It was well worth the trip, Dad.

Any time.

STING

DUH!

Can't have bees causing havoc on a descendant of The Duke of Wellington's land, can we?

STING

I've got a little something for you!

ARGH! I'm doomed! My head's goin' on that stand!

BLUSH!

Well, it's not as bad as I thought . . .

TROPHY ROOM

RECENT EXHIBITS INCLUDE:— A SMALL BEE BAGGED IN ONE'S GROUNDS

Blah! Blah! Drone!

GNU

KUDU

TAPIR

CLICK

. . . it's WORSE! How embarrassin'! Lemmedown, ya rotter!